CW00688102

Formed Stones', Folklore and Fossils

Michael G. Bassett

Department of Geology, National Museum of Wales, Cardiff

AMGUEDDFA GENEDLAETHOL CYMRU
NATIONAL MUSEUM OF WALES

Geological Series No. 1

CARDIFF, OCTOBER 1982

© National Museum of Wales 1982
ISBN 0 7200 0264 8

Designed by Penknife
Typeset by Afal
Printed by South Western Printers

Cover illustration
A snakestone – a fossil ammonite on which a head has been carved to make it resemble a serpent; the specimen belongs to the genus *Titanites,* from Upper Jurassic rocks of southern England.

Note
This booklet is a revised and expanded version of an article that was first published under the same title in *Amgueddfa, Bulletin of the National Museum of Wales,* No.7, Spring 1971, pp.2-17.

ssils are the remains or traces of animals and plants
at have been preserved by natural causes in the
ust of the Earth. Many have been familiar objects
man from well back into Stone Age times, and
er the years the different interpretations given to
em have produced some striking connotations in
k history. This article describes some of the better
own groups of fossils that are associated with
klore, both ancient and more modern, and
plains the origins of their colloquial names.
aphasis is placed on examples that have originated
Britain, but in a number of cases the opportunity
taken to draw attention to comparative examples
m other parts of the world as a means of
ustrating the similarity of beliefs and superstitions
er wide areas.

The scientific names of fossils, as of modern plants
d animals, are based on the genus and species
ncept established by the Swedish naturalist Carl
nnaeus in the tenth edition of his *Systema Naturae*
758). However, both long before and since that
ne many fossils have also been given distinctive
n-scientific or colloquial names, based either on a
asi-religious belief in their magical or medicinal
wers, or more frequently, on the direct
mparison of specimens with familiar every-day
jects. In an article in *Antiquity* the late
*. Kenneth Oakley described the archaeological
ociations of collections of fossils with the remains
early man and summarised the significance of
any of them in the following words: 'Although in
e earliest phases of culture certain fossils were
rhaps just regarded as "lucky", in more advanced
ases they would be thought to contain magical
wers, and then, as animism gives place to belief in
ds and ghosts, the fossil became a fetish, or
bitat of a god; finally, when the religion decayed
was replaced by another the fetish was no longer
object of specific belief, but degenerated in folk
emory to become regarded once again merely as an
ject conferring "good luck".' Many of the pre-
toric beliefs have passed into more recent folklore,
d with man's attempts to investigate the true
ture of fossils during historical times these early
liefs have been added to and reinterpreted. It was
ring this period of investigation that many of the
lloquial names were coined for certain fossils as
ey were related, correctly or incorrectly, to familiar
n-fossil objects.

By the middle of the 18th Century few educated
en did not believe in the organic origin of fossils,
t in the preceding 300 years the subject had been
e centre of major dispute among philosophers,
ologists and naturalists. The most widespread
edieval view was that fossils had originated from a
ative or plastic force *(vis plastica)* in the bowels of
the earth, while other theories suggested that they
arose from living seeds carried in vapours from the
sea, or that they were merely sports of nature.

In Britain during this period, theories such as
these were put forward or supported by a number of
scholars, of whom one of the most interesting was
Dr. Robert Plot (1640-1696), first Keeper of the
Ashmolean Museum in Oxford. In two large,
handsomely illustrated works, on *The Natural
History of Oxfordshire* (1677) and *The Natural
History of Staffordshire* (1686) he included chapters
on 'Formed Stones', the majority of which can be
recognised from his illustrations as fossil specimens.
Remarkably, Plot compared many of his 'formed
stones' with living organisms which are now known
to be their closely related descendants, but he was
never able to accept the organic origin of fossils.
He was certainly aware of contemporary arguments
in favour of organic theories for he discussed the
work of a number of authors, including the
Englishmen John Ray (1628-1705) and Robert Hooke
(1635-1703) and the Dane Niels Stensen
[Steno](1638-1687), all of whom were leading
proponents of the view. However, after some
deliberation Plot sided with the opinion of the
English zoologist and physician Martin Lister
(1638-1711) in concluding that fossils were 'Lapides
sui generis, *naturally produced by some
extraordinary* plastic virtue *latent* in the *Earth or
Quarries where they are found*' and that they 'seem
rather to be made for his [man's] *admiration*
than *use*'.

The value of Plot's two books lies not in their
scientific conclusions, but as records of contemporary
thinking and interpretation; in them he records
many of the descriptive and colloquial names
applied to fossil specimens in England at that time,
and for some which had previously been un-named
he even invented new terms that have themselves
been passed down over the years in folk history.

Rams' Horns, Snakestones and Conger Eels

The coiled shells of fossil ammonites have been
familiar to man since at least early Greek times, and
probably earlier. Ammonites belong to an extinct
group of cephalopod molluscs, distantly related to
the modern pearly *Nautilus* and even more distantly
to the squid and octopus. The distinctive coiling of
the ammonite shell suggested to the Greeks a
resemblance to the coiled horns of the ram which
was regarded as a sacred symbol, particularly
associated with the God *Jupiter Ammon*; specimens
thus became widely known as *Cornu Ammonis*
(horns of Ammon) and eventually in scientific terms
as ammonites. In China, coiled cephalopods of
various kinds, including ammonites, have also long

*Snakestones from Upper Lias (Jurassic) rocks near Whitby, Yorkshire. The specimens illustrate the two most common species from the area used for carving snakestone heads; the larger specimen (**left** and **centre**) is* Hildoceras bifrons *(specimen in the Yorkshire Museum); those on the right are* Dactylioceras commune. *The specimen at* **top right** *is particularly interesting in that it is the type specimen of the species – that is, it is the specimen to which the scientific name of the species was first given (by J. Sowerby in his* Mineral Conchology, *1815); it is now in the British Museum (Natural History), and although carved as a snakestone it forms the standard reference of comparison for the determination of this species (All x 1)*

been compared with horns, under the name *Jiao-shih* or *horn stones*.

Robert Plot described a number of *Cornu Ammonis* from Oxfordshire as being 'all so curled up within themselves, that the place of the head is always in the *circumference* and the *tail* in the *center* of the *stone*'. This description clearly illustrates the belief once held in many parts of the world that ammonites possessed heads and tails, despite the fact that they were never found preserved; coupled with this belief, the coiled shells most commonly suggested the form of a snake or serpent so that the name *Snakestones* became widely used to describe them.

In England the folklore of snakestones is centred mainly around Whitby in Yorkshire and Keynsham in Somerset. From near Whitby William Camden (1551-1623) in his *Britannia* of 1586 recorded stone which 'if you break them you find within stony serpents, wreathed up in circles, but generally without heads'. Legend supposes that the fossils we once living serpents which were common in the are until the 7th Century A.D. when the Saxon abbess St. Hilda (614-680) turned them into stone in orde to clear a site for the building of her convent. The heads of the serpents were assumed to have been destroyed on their death. This legend has passed into English literature as illustrated by the lowing passage from a poem by Surtees:

> Then sole amid the serpent tribe
> The holy Abbess stood,
> With fervent faith and uplift hands
> Grasping the holy rood.
> The suppliant's prayer and powerful charm
> Th'unnumber'd reptiles own;
> Each falling from the cliff, becomes
> A headless coil of stone.

similar passage from Sir Walter Scott's *Marmion* scribes the same tale:

> When Whitby's nuns exalting told,
> Of thousand snakes each one
> Was changed into a coil of stone,
> When holy Hilda pray'd;
> Themselves, within their holy ground,
> Their stony folds had often found.

e absence of heads in the Whitby snakestones is
metimes attributed to a further curse by
. Cuthbert, another saint from northern England.
order to perpetuate the legend and to effect sales
specimens, local collectors and dealers in fossils
quently 'restored' the snakestones by carving heads
. them. Many of the Whitby fossils were preserved
jet, which when carved and polished could make
autiful ornaments; the Vikings imported jet from
hitby, and at least one carving of an animal
sembling a snakestone is known from Norway,
ile in Elizabethan England snakestone brooches of
were highly prized.
With time the snakestone came to be regarded as
emblem of Whitby, probably sometime during
e 16th and 17th centuries. Tradesmen's tokens
aring a device of three snakestones are known from
far back as 1667, and in 1935 when Armorial
arings were officially granted to the town a similar
vice was incorporated in the Coat of Arms.

Another fine example of a snakestone from the Upper Lias of Whitby, carved from a specimen of Dactylioceras commune *preserved as jet (x 0.75 approx.; photograph by courtesy of Prof. J.E. Hemingway)*

Half-penny trade token with snakestone device, issued by Henry Sneaton of Flowergate in Whitby, 1667 (x 3)

illing trade token with snakestone device,
ued by the Whitby Association, 1811 (x 2)

The Coat of Arms of Whitby (by permission of Whitby Urban District Council)

The legend at Keynsham is similar to that at Whitby with, in this case, St. Keyna turning the serpents into stone. Elsewhere in southern England it was believed that snakestones were originally fairies, '. . . once the inhabitants of these parts, who for their crimes were changed, first into snakes, and then into stones'.

In some parts of the western isles of Scotland ammonites were once referred to as *Crampstones*. The evidence for this dates back to 1703 when M. Martin, in his *Description of the Western Islands of Scotland,* recorded that 'These Stones are by the Natives [of Syke] called Crampstones, because as they say they cure the Cramp in Cows, by washing the part affected with Water in which this Stone has been steep'd for some Hours'. Similar medicinal properties have been attributed to ammonites both in other parts of Britain and abroad. For example, in his *Survey of Cornwall* Richard Carew (1555-1620) reported that '. . . the *Snakes*, by their breathing about a hazell wand, doe make a stone ring of blew colour, in which there appeareth the yellow figure of a *Snake*; and that beasts which are stung, being given to drink of the water wherein this stone has been soaked, will therethrough recover'. And in the Harz mountains of Germany, Georg Henning Behrens (1662-1712) described in 1703 how farmers

WHITBY R.D.C. **WHITBY** **WHITBY U.D.C.**

Three variations of the heraldic device used as the Coat of Arms of Whitby, all incorporating snakestone symbols; the Arms of the Rural District Council were granted in 1958

om Gandersheim used as witchbane '. . . a fossile ɪaped like a Ram's Horn call'd Drake [Dragon]-ɪone . . . for when the Cows lose their milk, or void ɪood instead of it, they put these Stones into the ɪilk-pail, and by that means expect a due quantity ᶠ Milk from these Cows again'.

The *Ophites* of the ancient Greeks were clearly ɪnmonites, again used as a protection against snake ɪtes and as a cure for blindness, impotence and ɪarrenness. Some Australian aborigines today carry ɪnmonites to give them magical powers, while in ɪdia the same fossils are used as fetishes, being ɪaced in Hindu temples as representations of the ᶠod Vishnu. Throughout India, ammonites are ɪnown as *salagrams* or *salagramma* and in Vishnu ɪlts from at least the 5th Century B.C. they have ɪen used steeped in water as a draft to wash away ɪns. In North America, medicine men of the many ɪibes of Plains Indians and of the Navajos carried ɪnmonites in their medicine bags; to these people ɪnmonites were known as *wanisugna*, meaning 'life ɪithin the seed, seed within the shell'. To the ɪlackfoot Indians ammonites resembled sleeping ɪson and were thus called *iniskim* or *buffalo stones,* ɪsed in spiritual ceremonies prior to the hunting and ɪoralling of bison herds.

Among the largest ammonites known are a number ᶠ species found in the Portland Stone (Jurassic) of ɪorset and Wiltshire. One particular genus, ɪitanites, is often represented by shells reaching two ɪet or more in diameter and one of its species is ɪamed *Titanites giganteus* as an allusion to its large ɪze. To the quarrymen of the Isle of Portland these ɪrge, coiled shells resemble 'sea-serpents' or eels and ɪave thus been given the local name of *Conger Eels*. ɪhildren in this area play 'hopscotch' on stone slabs ɪat cut through the large ammonites to reveal them ɪ cross-section, with the chalked lines of ɪonventional forms of the game represented by the ɪalls of the chambers that spiral outwards from the ɪentre of the fossil.

ɪmmonites and Architecture

ɪhe county of Sussex in the south of England has a ɪarticular and distinctive association of ammonites ɪith every day life, dating from the early 19th ɪentury Regency Period when designs based on these ɪssils were incorporated in the façades of fashionable ɪouses. Known today as the 'Ammonite Order' in ɪrchitecture, the designs feature pilasters with ɪpitals whose volutes were cast in the form of large ɪnmonites, clearly as a variation on classical Ionic ɪpitals. Records suggest that the 'Order' originated ɪ London, devised by an architect named George ɪance who used it in 1789 to decorate the frontage ᶠ the former Shakespeare Gallery, erected on the

north side of Pall Mall (No. 52) for Alderman Boydell, a well known print dealer. The building was demolished in 1868, but a number of engravings exist showing the paired, plain pilasters and 'ammonite capitals'.

The ammonite design came to the attention of a builder-cum-architect from Lewes in Sussex named Amon Wilds, who incorporated it in the façade of houses at No. 2 and No. 3 Castle Place in Lewes, built in about 1810. There seems little reason to doubt that Wilds was attracted to the 'Ammonite Order' as much by the punning allusion to his Christian name as by the architectural merits.

The houses in Castle Place also have a further association with geology, since No. 3 was bought in 1816 by the Sussex doctor and palaeontologist Gideon Mantell, and three years later he then bought No. 2 from Amon Wilds and converted them into a single house. Whether Mantell was attracted or influenced by the 'ammonite capitals' in purchasing these houses is not known, but with his knowledge of fossils he may well have been (the combined houses in Castle Place now form 166 High Street, Lewes).

Together with his son Amon Henry Wilds, also an architect, Amon Wilds senior left Lewes in 1815 and settled in Brighton, and from 1820 onwards all their work was in the latter town. In 1822 they were joined by a third partner, Charles Augustus Busby. The firm of Wilds and Busby rapidly established itself and was responsible for much of the creation of 'Regency Brighton' during the 1820s and early 1830s. Ammonite capitals became virtually a 'trade mark' of the firm, particularly in many of the houses designed by Amon Henry Wilds. The capitals are all identical or virtually identical to those used earlier in Lewes. Visitors to Brighton today can still enjoy the elegance of the 'Ammonite Order', some of the best examples being preserved in Oriental Place, Old Steine, Hanover Crescent, Montpelier Crescent, Montpelier Road, and Preston Street.

Thunderbolts, Bat Stones and Gnomes' Candles

The pointed, internal guards of fossil belemnites which occur commonly in Jurassic and Cretaceous rocks have long been referred to in folklore as *Thunderbolts*. Belemnites are an extinct group of cephalopods related to the modern cuttlefish, but with their cylindrical, pointed or arrow-shaped outline they have been interpreted widely as having been flung down as darts from heaven during thunderstorms. Plot described them as having 'the form of *arrow heads,* and thought by the vulgar to be indeed the darts of *Heaven*: which . . . I have placed among the *stones* related to the *Heavens*'. In some regions the same fossils are known also as

Devil's Fingers or *St. Peter's Fingers*, while in parts of south-east England they are sometimes called *bullets*. The widespread notion that belemnites were related in some way to lightning seems to have been heightened by the translucent nature and pale yellowish to bluish colour of many specimens, perhaps resembling the colour produced during a lightning flash. Even the word belemnite itself, derived from the Greek *belemnon*, meaning *dart*, is an allusion to the derivation of these fossils as bolts from the heavens. The Chinese term *Jien-shih*, meaning *sword stone*, possibly refers to the same belief.

Specimens of belemnites from the Jurassic rocks of Whitby are known locally as *scaur pencils*. The pencil refers to the obvious shape, while the Scaur is the name of the inter-tidal platform of shales that extends for about a mile to the east of the town, and from these relatively soft shales the belemnites are often weathered out to be easily collected.

Perhaps more than any other group of fossils in Britain belemnites have been thought to have medicinal powers. In parts of western Scotland, where they were once known as *Bat Stones*, they were believed to cure horses of worms which caused distemper, the remedy being to give the horses water to drink in which specimens had been soaked for some time. In southern England they have been variously regarded as cures for rheumatism and sore eyes in both men and horses; in the latter case the treatment involved the crushing of the fossils to produce a dust which was then blown into the eyes.

In Scandinavia, belemnites were once regarded as candles belonging to elves, pixies, or gnomes, and in many areas they are still named popularly as *vätteljus* (Swedish – literally *gnomes' lights* or *candles*).

Swedish Nails and Chinese Pagodas

On his journey through the island of Öland in June 1741, Linnaeus recorded the presence of fossils known locally as *Ölandsspikar* from limestones in the area around Böda. The limestones are of Ordovician age and the fossils referred to were straight nautiloid cephalopods resembling spikes or nails; the local name means *Öland spikes* or *Öland nails*. Unlike their modern coiled descendant *Nautilus*, the early nautiloids mostly had straight or only very gently curved shells that tapered gradually towards the

Thunderbolts (fossil belemnites) from the Lower Jurassic, central England (x 0.75 approx.)

(left) *'Ammonite capitals'.* **A**, **B**, **C** *and* **D**, *No.166 High St., Lewes (formerly Castle Place);* **C** *shows details of the classical Ionic capitals on the same house.* **E**, *a magnificent row of capitals on Nos.8-10 Oriental Place, Brighton.* **F** *and* **G**, *No.26 Old Steine [Steyne], Brighton.* **H** *and* **I**, *No.25 Oriental Place, Brighton. Note the identical design of the capitals on all the buildings, probably denoting casting from the same mould or set of moulds*

Semi-diagrammatic drawing of an Ordovician orthoconic nautiloid in longitudinal section to show the chambered interior; the curved transverse walls or septa are the structures that give the impression of a Chinese pagoda in this orientation. The life orientation of these animals was horizontal and the shells grew forward from the narrow (proximal) end

proximal end. The straight forms are known as orthocones, and they vary in length from a few centimetres to about 5 metres in some Ordovician specimens of the genus *Endoceras*; many of the Öland specimens are related to this genus.

As in all nautiloids, the orthoconic forms have a chambered internal structure, with transverse walls that vary from straight to curved. Sections through these fossils often reveal the successive chambers and walls with their connecting tube for the siphuncle, and in certain orientations such sections have been taken in parts of China to resemble the shape of the vertical succession of roofs on a pagoda. The Chinese colloquial name for these fossils is *Bao-ta-shih*, meaning *pagoda stone*.

The Devil's Toenail

To both the layman and the professional geologist the fossil oyster *Gryphaea arcuata* is one of the most easily recognisable species in Britain. It occurs very commonly in Lower Lias (Jurassic) rocks throughout the country and its evolutionary history has been the subject of spirited controversy among palaeontologists since the 1920s. Long before that, however, its characteristic incurved shape was familiar to many and it has become widely known as the *Devil's toenail*.

Gryphaea is a bivalved mollusc ancestral to the modern oyster and related to other bivalves such as clams and mussels, but unlike most of its near relatives its two valves are of unequal size. The larger, incurved, left valve was the one on which the animal sat and attached itself to the sea floor, with the small, flat, right valve then acting as a kind of lid to the shell. The ancestors of *Gryphaea* had two flat, equal-sized valves and lived on a fairly hard sea floor, but in early Jurassic times conditions over much of Britain changed fairly rapidly and the sea floor at

times became covered in layers of soft mud. In order to survive, the *Gryphaea* ancestors adapted rapidly to the new conditions by raising the margin of the valves above the mud in order to avoid suffocation and to ensure a flow of clean, food-bearing water. The quickest way of achieving this was for the left valve to become strongly incurved, with a complementary reduction in size of the right valve to produce the distinctive shape of *Gryphaea arcuata*.

One of Robert Plot's 'formed stones' from Oxfordshire was described by him as being 'of the *Oyster* kind . . . of an *oblong figure*, very thick, and of a bluish colour'; the specimen is readily identified as a *Gryphaea*. Even at that time these shells had received distinctive names in some parts of the country, for Plot further records that his specimen 'may be the same with the petrified *Concha oblonga crassa*, mentioned by Dr. *Merret*, found in *Worcester-shire*, and there called *Crow-stones, Crow-cups*, or *Egg-stones*'.

In Scotland too *Gryphaea* has its associations in folklore, being named in Gaelic *clach crubain* or crouching shell. According to some 17th and 18th Century reports in Scotland, the possession of a

Devils' toenails; Gryphaea arcuata, *Lower Lias (Jurassic), Gloucestershire (x 0.75 approx.)*

REFULGET·LABORES·NOSTROS·COELUM

The Coat of Arms of Scunthorpe (by permission of the Borough of Scunthorpe)

specimen guaranteed a cure for arthritis or other pains in the bones. As Oakley has observed, this would appear to be a clear case of sympathetic magic, based on the hope that the distorted shape of the shells would in some way help to prevent similar distortion in the owner.

Since 1936 illustrations of *Gryphaea* have been incorporated in the coat of arms of the Borough of Scunthorpe. The fossil occurs commonly in the Jurassic ironstone deposits in the neighbourhood and its incorporation in the design signifies the importance of the iron and steel industry in the commercial life of the town.

Osses 'Eds

Among the most amusing of Plot's 'formed stones' are those 'that resemble the parts of *four footed beasts*'. One particular specimen, described from Headington in Oxfordshire, was 'the most like to the head of a Horse of any thing I can think of; having the *ears,* and *crest* of the *mane* appearing between them, the places of the *eyes* suitably prominent, and the rest of the *face* entire, only the *mouth* and *nostrils* are absent in them all'. The quarries at Headington are well known for their rich fossil faunas of Corallian (Jurassic) age and Plot's illustration and description allow his specimen to be identified as the bivalled mollusc *Myophorella [Trigonia] hudlestoni*, a species which occurs commonly in the area. Unlike *Gryphaea,* mentioned earlier, *Myophorella* is a regular bivalve with two equal-sized valves. The preservation at Headington is usually in the form of natural moulds of the interior of the valves, and when such a mould is orientated obliquely it becomes immediately obvious why Plot compared his specimen with a horse's head. The large 'eyes' are represented by the distinctive muscle impressions on the mould, the 'ears' by the configuration of the beaks of the shell, and the 'mane' by the ridged appearance of the teeth and sockets used in the interlocking and the opening and closing of the valves. As no one had previously named any similar 'formed stones' Plot called them *Hippocephaloides* as an allusion to their obvious shape.

To what extent Plot's name became generally used is not certain, but on the Isle of Portland in Dorset bivalves closely resembling those from Headington are similarly referred to by quarrymen as *horses heads*. In this case the name is applied to the moulds of a slightly different species, *Myophorella [Trigonia] incurva*, which is found abundantly in the Portland Stone; a second species *Laevitrigonia gibbosa* also occurs in the same beds, and since the moulds are often difficult to separate from those of *Myophorella* it too is often given the same colloquial name. The Dorsetshire dialect of the quarrymen reduces the 'horses heads' to the more familiar sound of *'osses 'eds.*

Bulls Hearts

The same quarry at Headington from which he described his *Hippocephaloides* also provided Robert Plot with other likenesses of parts of 'four footed beasts' that he identified as '*Cardites*, or *stones* in the form of *hearts*, but by *Authors*, because of their bigness, generally called *Bucardites*, or stones like *Bulls hearts*'. Plot's illustration is readily identified as the smooth internal mould of another bivalve mollusc belonging to the genus *Protocardia*, shown in lateral view so that the inflated valves and incurved beaks do indeed resemble a heart in shape.

Osses 'Eds; Robert Plot's Hippocephaloides **(left)**, *from* The Natural History of Oxfordshire, *with two views of* Myophorella incurva *from the Portland Stone (Upper Jurassic), Dorset, showing an oblique view* **(centre)** *to compare with Plot's figure, and the conventional orientation* **(right)** *(x 0.75 approx.)*

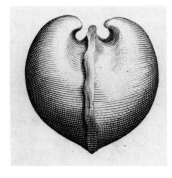

Bulls Hearts; Robert Plot's Bucardites *from Headington* (**left**), *from* The Natural History of Oxfordshire, *with two views of a similar* Protocardia *from the Jurassic of Shotover, Oxfordshire, showing a lateral view* (**centre**) *to compare with Plot's figure, and the conventional orientation* (**right**) *(x 0.75 approx.)*

From nearby Brize Norton and Witney, in rocks of roughly the same age, Plot recorded other *Bucardites* 'that seem to be ribbed on each side', one of which was 'ten inches round, and near two pounds in weight'. These ribbed 'bulls hearts' are also identifiable as *Protocardia*, but in this case the specimens were preserved not as internal moulds but as shells with the external ribbing intact. Plot was unable to appreciate the significance of the different modes of preservation of the same types of fossils.

Screwstones and St. Cuthbert's Beads
Two quite different and unrelated groups of fossils are referred to colloquially in Britain as *Screwstones*. In some parts of southern England the term is used for a number of spirally coiled univalved molluscs known as gastropods, of which the modern whelk is a good living example. In the fossil state the resemblance of these shells to a screw thread becomes even more pronounced when the shell material itself has been destroyed after the infilling of the interior with sediment to form a natural mould. The best known screwstones are from Jurassic rocks, notably the Great Oolite around Bath and the Portland Stone of Dorset, both of which are used extensively as building stone. On the Isle of Portland many gastropods occur throughout the succession, but the quarrymen reserve the term screwstone almost exclusively for the moulds of a single species from the Portland Stone known as *Aptyxiella portlandica*. The abundance of this species and its familiarity to quarrymen and geologists alike have led to its becoming known as the *Portland Screw*.

In Derbyshire and other parts of the English Midlands the term screwstone is reserved for the internal moulds of the stems of fossil crinoids, notably from the Carboniferous Limestone. Both

Portland Screws; Aptyxiella portlandica *from the Portland Stone, Dorset (x 1.5 approx.)*

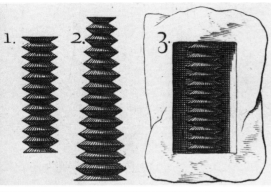

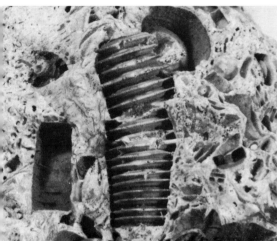

modern and fossil crinoids superficially resemble some types of plants, to the extent that they are often referred to colloquially as *sea-lilies,* but they are in fact animals with calcareous hard parts, of which the stem is most commonly preserved in the fossil state. The numerous superposed disc-shaped columnals making up the stem are perforated by an axial canal which frequently became infilled by sediment on the death of the animal, and subsequent solution of the surrounding calcareous shell material left the infilling material as an internal mould. In specimens from Derbyshire, moulds such as these have a distinctive screw-thread appearance, the specimens being known to quarrymen as *Derbyshire Screws.*

From Staffordshire Plot described similar specimens as screwstones, but he failed to realise that they represented the axial infillings of other 'formed stones', for he differentiated them from unaltered crinoid stems which he described as *'Entrochi* or wheels within wheels'. In the same passage he referred to individual columnals from the stems which had long been used as beads, often strung together to form a necklace or rosary; in many parts of the country these are known as *St. Cuthbert's beads*, named after the same St. Cuthbert of northern England who is associated with the legend of the Whitby snakestones. St. Cuthbert's monastic retreat is generally supposed to have been on the island of Lindisfarne [Holy Island] off the coast of Northumberland, and it is from that island that the legend of threading crinoid columnals as a rosary is best known, particularly in the following passage from Sir Walter Scott's *Marmion*:

> But fain Saint Hilda's nuns would learn
> If, on a rock by Lindisfarne,
> Saint Cuthbert sits, and toils to frame
> The sea-born beads that bear his name.

A small islet on the south side of Lindisfarne, connected to the main island at low tide and known locally as St. Cuthbert's Isle, may have been the true location of the cell. It is interesting that shales between Lindisfarne and St. Cuthbert's Isle yield abundant crinoid stems that often weather out freely from the rock, and would therefore have been much more readily collected than specimens from the massive crinoidal limestone of the main island itself.

In some other parts of England, rounded crinoid

Three of Plot's screwstones (top), *from* The Natural History of Staffordshire, *with a Derbyshire Screw* (centre) *from the Carboniferous Limestone, Derbyshire, for comparison (x 1 approx.) and two unaltered crinoid stems* (bottom) *showing the numerous columnals, also from Derbyshire (x 1 approx.)*

columnals were once referred to as *fairy money*, while in Germany they were named similarly as *St. Boniface's pennies (Bonifacius Pfennige)*.

Star-Stones

The *Star-stones* or *Asteriae* of Robert Plot were recognised by him as consisting of two distinct groups – 'those, whose whole Bodies make the form of a Star, . . . in opposition to the *Astroites,* which in the whole are irregular, but adorned as it were with a *Constellation'*. Both were considered to 'relate to the *Heavenly Bodies* or *Air'* and both can now be identified with separate groups of fossils.

In the first category he included crinoid stems, related to those described above as screwstones, but differing in having a distinctive pentagonal or star-shaped cross-section. Similar specimens were figured in the accounts of Oxfordshire and Staffordshire; in the former case the specimens can be identified provisionally as the Jurassic genus *Pentacrinites*. They were described by Plot as consisting of 'thin lamellae or plates, lying obliquely to the *Horizontal* position of the star' the whole making up a '*pentagonous cylindrical column'*. He clearly experimented to separate the individual columnals from one another and discovered that 'if but steeped a night in *vinegar,* or other sharp liquor, [they] may be divided the next morning with safety and ease'. He also reported that the same phenomenon was known to Roger Bacon nearly 400 years previously. This may well be the first record of attempts to clean and separate fossils from their matrix, albeit in ignorance of their nature; it is interesting to note that acid is used by palaeontologists today in order to isolate fossils of certain compositions from their matrix.

The second group, referred to by Plot as the *Astroites* or *starry-stones,* belong mainly to fossil corals. From Oxfordshire he described four different types, at least two of which can be tentatively identified with the Jurassic genera *Isastrea* and *Cyathophora*. Later, in his account of Staffordshire he compared other specimens, of probable Carboniferous age, with 'porous *Species* of *Coral'* or '*Madreporae'*, but in this case he was discussing their similarity not to the star-stones but to the formed stones 'relating to the *vegetable Kingdom'*.

The comparison of fossil corals with the stars becomes especially apparent when specimens are cut and polished to bring out the pattern of the septa, which in life formed calcareous supports for the soft parts of the animal. One of the best known species

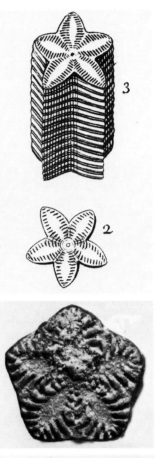

A Star-Stone (top) *from* The Natural History of Oxfordshire, *with corresponding views* (centre *and* bottom) *of the stem of the crinoid* Pentacrinites fossilis *from the Lower Lias, Dorset (x 3 approx.)*

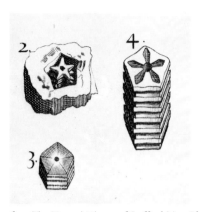

Star-Stones from The Natural History of Staffordshire. *Plot compared these specimens (crinoid columnals of probable Carboniferous age) with 'the* towel *of a* Spur', *and described them in some detail; unlike specimens from Oxfordshire he did not consider that these had lamellae or plates lying oblique to the position of the star.*

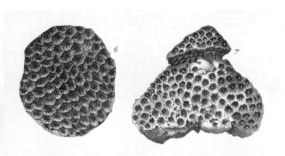

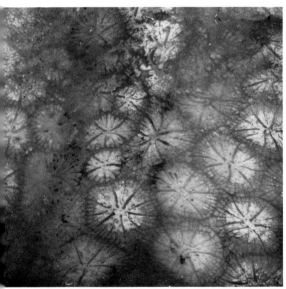

Asteriae or Star-Stones; fossil corals from The Natural History of Oxfordshire *(top), and a polished section (bottom) of* Isastrea oblonga – *the Tisbury starstone, from the Portland beds, Tisbury, Wiltshire (x 3 approx.)*

with a distinctive star pattern is *Isastrea oblonga* which occurs commonly in the Portland (Jurassic) beds of southern England; it is particularly well preserved around Tisbury in Wiltshire, where specimens are frequently silicified and are capable of being highly polished. The common occurrence of the species in the area has led to it becoming known locally as the *Tisbury starstone* or *starry agate*.

Shepherds' Crowns and Fairy Loaves

The spiny shelled echinoids or sea-urchins are familiar objects on many beaches, where they are washed up on death from their habitats on the sea floor. Usually the spines of dead echinoids become detached from the shell very quickly so that in fossil specimens they are not often preserved. Plot described a wide variety of fossil echinoids and discussed their resemblance to modern sea-urchins, but could not agree on any relationship. Instead he recorded his fossils by a number of names including '*Histricites*, or *Porcupine-stone* without bristles'. To modern echinoids he applied the names 'sea *Hedg-hogs* . . . *sea Thistles* . . . or *sea Apples*'.

Among the best preserved echinoids to be found in Britain are those from the Cretaceous chalk of the downlands of southern England, where the shells are commonly in the form of flint casts. To prehistoric man in the area the fossils were clearly of religious significance, as witnessed by the discovery of nearly 100 specimens arranged in circles around the bodies of a woman and child in an Early Bronze Age tumulus on Dunstable Down.

More recent folklore is centred mainly around two genera of echinoids, *Micraster* and *Echinocorys*. The latter has a distinctive helmet- or crown-shape and is frequently referred to as the *Shepherds' crown*; the reasons for this are presumably related to specimens being found commonly by shepherds who would be likely to come across them weathered from the chalk while tending their sheep on the downs. The comparison with a crown may well have been heightened by interpreting the five double rows of pores preserved on the echinoid shell as the supporting arms of the crowns similar to those worn by the monarchy in Medieval England.

Micraster is a heart-shaped echinoid which, together with *Echinocorys*, is sometimes known as a *Fairy loaf*. They were possibly once regarded as loaves belonging to the fairies, but more recent superstition suggested that if specimens were kept in the house the family would never go short of bread. In parts of southern England fossil sea-urchins have also been thought to prevent milk from going sour and in some places are still traditionally placed on dairy shelves.

The folklore of fossil echinoids is also particularly

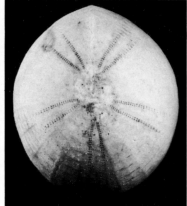

Shepherds' Crowns and Fairy Loaves; Echinocorys scutata (**left** *and* **centre**) *and* Micraster coranguinum (**bottom**), *from the Upper Chalk, south of England (x 1 approx.)*

strong in parts of Denmark, where they have long been regarded as thunderstones or thunderbolts from heaven. Even today they are placed in houses and other buildings as a protection against lightning and to act as charms against various forms of witchcraft. Plot mentioned a similar interpretation of echinoids as thunderbolts in his account of Oxfordshire. This belief possibly stems from the superficial resemblance of the rough surface of some echinoids to nodules of the mineral iron pyrites, which have also been regarded in many areas as stones from heaven.

Snakes' Eggs and Jew-Stones

Belief in the mystical or protective powers of fossil echinoids such as those described immediately above has long extended in many areas into a belief that they also have strong medicinal properties. Some Cretaceous echinoids from Kent, filled with the fine chalk of the area, were once known as *Chalk-eggs* and were ground up and used by British seamen as 'remedies for subduing acrid humours of the stomach'.

It is generally agreed that the *'snakes' eggs'* first described by the Roman historian Pliny the Elder (23-79 A.D.) in his *Natural History* were fossil sea-urchins of various kinds that were considered to form powerful antidotes against snake poison. According to Pliny, an ancient Celtic tradition reported by the Druids of Gaul supposed that certain stones originated as balls of froth exuded by numerous entwined snakes at midsummer. Such a ball was called an *ovum anguinum*. It was tossed into the air by the snakes, and if it could be caught in a cloth before hitting the ground then it retained great magical powers; the captor was not safe at least until he had crossed a river through which the snakes

Medieval woodcut (1497) illustrating the 'capture' of an Ovum anguinum

16

could not swim. In addition to protection from poison and other illnesses, possession of these specimens was reputed to ensure success in battle and in disputes of many kinds. The roughened ambulacral areas of the echinoids were thought to represent the marks where snakes had been attached to the surface. The Celtic 'snake's egg' (or *adderstone* as it is known in some regions) was called *glain naidr* in Wales, and *milprev* or *milpref* in Cornwall.

Pliny also described some stones from Palestine as *Tecolithi* and said that licking such objects was a means of helping to dissolve gallstones. These specimens can be identified as the thick, club- or bladder-shaped spines of the Cretaceous echinoid *Balanocidaris*. During the Crusades many such spines were brought back to Europe, where they eventually became known as *Lapidus Judaici* or 'stones from Judea', and with time they were commonly called *Jew-stones*. They were also referred to colloquially as *petrified olives*. Their superficial resemblance to a bladder is a further example of the principle of sympathetic magic in using them (powdered in water) for the treatment of gall, bladder and kidney ailments.

A Jew-Stone; the spine of the echinoid Balanocidaris glandaria *from Cretaceous rocks of the eastern Mediterranean region*

Crystal Apples

Just as Robert Plot compared some modern echinoderms with apples, so in parts of Sweden have a related fossil group long been likened to the same fruit. The fossils in question are cystoids, an extinct group of globular echinoderms known only from rocks of Ordovician to Devonian age. They are particularly common in Ordovician strata in different areas of central and southern Sweden, especially in Dalarna, Västergötland, and on the island of Öland. In his travels through these areas in the mid 1700s Linnaeus commented on the occurrence of *kalkbollar (lime balls)* or *kristalläpplen (crystal apples),* and recognised that the same species occurred in the different regions. The term *kristalläpplen* is still used colloquially today for these fossils but reserved almost entirely for the two most common cystoid species, *Sphaeronites pomum* and *Echinosphaerites aurantium;* the species name of the former is clearly an allusion to the colloquial name of the group.

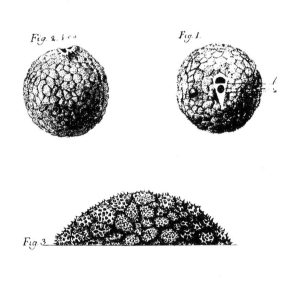

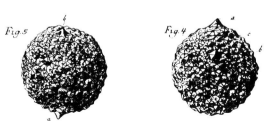

The Dudley Locust

Of all groups of invertebrate fossils, perhaps the best known and most attractive to the layman are the trilobites, an extinct group of marine arthropods which are distantly related to a variety of modern animals such as crabs, crayfish and woodlice. Their distinctive segmented and trilobed morphology makes them particularly easy to recognise and they are frequently found in abundance in Palaeozoic

Crystal Apples; illustrations of Ordovician cystoids from Sweden described in 1772 by J.A. Gyllenhaal, who was the first to recognise the organic nature of these fossils. The upper three figures are Sphaeronites pomum *and the lower two are* Echinosphaerites aurantium

Three views of The Dudley Locust, Calymene blumenbachii, *from the Much Wenlock Limestone Formation, Dudley (x 1 approx.)*

rocks. At one locality in Bron-y-Buckley Wood at Welshpool, Powys, trilobites are so common that in *The Silurian System* (1839) Sir Roderick Murchison named the spot *Trilobite Dingle,* a name which is still in use today.

In Britain one particular trilobite species, known as *Calymene blumenbachii,* has attracted more public attention than any other; it occurs fairly commonly in Silurian rocks in many parts of the country but is nowhere more common or better preserved than in the Much Wenlock Limestone Formation at Dudley in the West Midlands. Limestone is known to have been quarried for lime on a small scale at Dudley at least as far back as the middle of the 17th Century, but with the coming of the Industrial Revolution in the late 18th and 19th centuries enormous quantities were removed for use as flux in the rapidly growing iron industry. The Much Wenlock Limestone at Dudley is extremely rich in fossil remains, and during quarrying operations the quarrymen were able to collect countless numbers of specimens. Well preserved examples of *Calymene blumenbachii* were especially common, some of which showed the trilobites in a curled-up position, doubtless reminding the quarrymen of the similar habit of woodlice, while the uncurled specimens resembled other arthropods such as beetles and insects; this species became so familiar to the men that in time it became known as the *Dudley Locust* or *Dudley Insect.*

The superb preservation and abundance of fossils from Dudley soon attracted wide attention and created a demand from collectors throughout the world. Complete specimens of trilobites were especially sought after, but as often as not the process of fossilisation had led to the separation of the heads, bodies and tails. The quarrymen and professional collectors who set up shops to sell fossils soon realised that perfect specimens would fetch the highest prices; in some cases they therefore carefully pieced together the different parts of unrelated specimens to produce an artificial, but often perfect looking 'trilobite'.

The Dudley Locust became so well known in the 19th Century that with time it came to be regarded as an emblem of the town. The exact dating of this is uncertain but the fossil was certainly included in a device used as the Common Seal of the Corporation as far back as 1866. In 1957 the College of Heralds granted Armorial Bearings to Dudley which incorporated the device from the Common Seal, and so the Dudley Locust now has a permanent place in the town's coat of arms.

The popularity of trilobites in 19th Century Britain was not confined to the Dudley region or restricted to natural historians. This was part of a 'Golden Age' of geology and palaeontology which brought the significance of fossils to a wide sector of the general public, particularly because of the crucial evidence that they brought to the debate on evolution. That trilobites had become familiar to the public is illustrated by the following poem which appeared in the popular journal *Punch* in January 1885; entitled *The Lay of the Trilobite,* it relates a conversation with a trilobite on the course of evolution. The accompanying cartoon shows T.H. Huxley, the champion of Charles Darwin's theory of evolution, holding this conversation. It seems immaterial that the illustration is not of a trilobite but of another fossil arthropod called a eurypterid; niceties of the differences between the two groups were presumably lost on both the cartoonist and the public alike!

> A MOUNTAIN'S giddy height I sought,
> Because I could not find
> Sufficient vague and mighty thought
> To fill my mighty mind.

E. HOLLIER,

DUDLEY,

HAS FOR SALE A LARGE SELECTION OF

Silurian Trilobites, Crinoids,

CORALS, SHELLS, &C.,

From the Wenlock Shale and Limestone, &c., in the neighbourhood of Dudley.

——:o:——

E. H. will be pleased to show (when convenient) to any party who may be interested in their inspection, one of the finest collections of Trilobites, &c., in the kingdom, together with other rare Fossil specimens.

OFFICE, STONE STREET; PRIVATE RESIDENCE, KING EDMUND PLACE

DUDLEY.

An advertisement announcing the sale of Silurian fossils from Dudley. The advertiser, E. Hollier, was a chemist and a former mayor of the town. (From The Curiosities of Dudley and the Black Country, *1881)*

The Coat of Arms of Dudley (by permission of the County Borough of Dudley)

THE LAY OF THE TRILOBITE.

T.H. Huxley discussing evolution with a 'trilobite'; cartoon from Punch, or The London Charivari, *January 24th, 1885*

And, as I wandered ill at ease,
There chanced upon my sight,
A native of Silurian seas, –
An ancient Trilobite!

So calm, so peacefully he lay,
I watched him e'en with tears
I thought of Monads far away,
In the forgotten years.
How wonderful it seemed, and right
The providential plan,
That he should be a Trilobite,
And I should be a Man!

And then, quite natural and free,
Out of his rocky bed,
That Trilobite he spoke to me,
And this is what he said:
'I don't know how the thing was done,
Although I cannot doubt it;
But HUXLEY, – he if any one
Can tell you all about it:—

'How all your faiths are ghosts and dreams,
How, in the silent sea,
Your ancestors were Monotremes –
Whatever these may be, –
How you evolved your shining lights
Of wisdom and perfection,
From Jelly-fish and Trilobites,
By Natural Selection.

'You've KANT to make your brains go round,
And CARPENTER to clear them,
And Mathematics to confound,
And Mr. Punch to cheer them.
The native of an alien land
You call a man and brother,
And greet with pistol in one hand,
and hymn-book in the other!

'You've Politics to make you fight,
And utter exclamations,
You've cannon, and you've dynamite,
To civilise the nations.
The side that makes the loudest din
Is surest to be right,
And oh, a pretty fix you're in!'
remarked the Trilobite.

'But gentle, stupid, free from woe,
I dwelt among my nation,
I didn't care, I didn't know,
That I was a crustacean;
I didn't grumble, didn't steal,
I never took to rhyme,

Salt water was my frugal meal,
With carbonate of lime.'

Reluctantly I turned away,
No other word he said;
An ancient Trilobite he lay
Within his rocky bed.
I did not answer him, for that
Would have annoyed my pride,
I merely bowed, and touched my hat,
But in my heart I cried –

'I wish our brains were not so good,
I wish our skulls were thicker,
I wish that Evolution could
Have stopped a little quicker,
For oh, it was a happy plight
Of liberty and ease,
To be a simple Trilobite
In the Silurian Seas.'

In keeping with the interpretation of the *Dudley Locust,* trilobites in some other parts of the world have also been named popularly after small flying animals such as bats and butterflies. For example, in parts of China the spiny tails of some species are called *Bien-fu-shih (bat stones),* while forms with a long pair of spines are differentiated as *Hu-die-shih (butterfly stones).* In the Carmarthen district of South Wales, the tails of some Ordovician trilobites were once considered to represent 'petrified butterflies', resulting from spells cast by the magician Merlin of Arthurian legends. The allusion to butterflies is also reflected in the Swedish term *fjärilssten*, which is applied particularly to the heads and tails of large species of *Eobronteus* and *Platylichas* from mounds of the Ordovician Böda Limestone in Dalarna. A quite different name is given to some Lower Ordovician asaphid trilobites on the Swedish island of Öland; these forms have large, flattened heads and tails that are compared locally with flat-fish and called *flundra (flounders).*

Not surprisingly, trilobites were once of mystical significance to some peoples and there are a number of records from various areas of specimens associated with the remains of pre-historic man. In the 1800s the Pahvant Ute Indians of western Utah, U.S.A. are known to have collected one particular species, *Elrathia kingii,* from Middle Cambrian rocks at Wheeler Amphitheatre in the northern House Range, where many fine examples can still be collected today. Some specimens weather out completely free from the rock and were known to the Indians as *shugi-pits napa t'schoy,* meaning *lizard foot bead things;* other specimens preserved in the rock matrix were called *timpe khanitza pachavee,*

Pahvant Indian necklace from Utah, U.S.A., incorporating specimens of Elrathia kingii; *made for Mr. F.A. Beckwith by T.N. Pickyavit in 1931 (photograph by courtesy of Dr. M.E. Taylor)*

Hu-die-shih *(butterfly stone)* **(above)** *and* Bien-fu-shih *(bat stone)* **(below)**. *Both are tails of trilobites from the Upper Cambrian Kushan Formation, Yenchuang, Shantung, China; the upper specimen is* Drepanura premesnili *and the lower one is* Blackwelderia sinensis *(both x 2 approx.)*

meaning *little water bug like stone house in*. The former name and preservation reflects the use of these trilobites in amulets and necklaces as a means of warding off evil spirits and to give protection in battle. The latter name possibly indicates that the Pahvants recognised the organic origin of the fossils by comparing them with aquatic insects of various kinds.

The Delabole Butterfly

The slate industry of north west Cornwall is restricted to a belt of Upper Devonian rocks between Tintagel and Camelford. In the past there were numerous small quarries throughout the area, but with the decline in the use of slates for roofing the industry is now virtually confined to the small village of Delabole, two miles west of Camelford. Slate quarrying has been carried on at Delabole since at least the 16th Century and the huge Old Delabole Quarry is probably the largest slate quarry in the world. Fossils are comparatively rare in the slates and those that are found have been flattened and distorted by the pressures set up by earth movements

in the period when the slate was formed by slight alteration from original beds of shale. However, the fine-grained, homogeneous composition of the slates has allowed even the flattened fossils to be preserved in remarkable detail.

Of those fossils that are present in the Cornish slates one of the most common, and certainly the most famous, is the brachiopod species *Cyrtospirifer verneuili*. The brachiopods are a group of bivalved shells represented in modern seas by relatively few species, but found commonly as fossils throughout most of the geological column. *Cyrtospirifer* belongs to a wide-hinged group of brachiopods known as the spiriferids, and in specimens from Cornwall the distortion has often led to an apparent lateral elongation of the hinge to produce a distinctive 'winged' appearance in the fossils. To the quarrymen these winged fossils resembled butterflies and since many of the specimens collected in the past were from Old Delabole Quarry the species came to be known as the *Delabole Butterfly*.

Wide-hinged spiriferid brachiopods have been interpreted similarly in China since at least the 4th Century A.D. There, undistorted specimens of the genera *Cyrtospirifer* and *Sinospirifer* have wing-like hinges resembling the outstretched wings of a bird, with the result that they are known as *Shih-yen* or *stone-swallows*. Some species of *Shih-yen* are known only from apothecaries' shops, for these fossils are still used widely in medicine in parts of China; they are boiled in water with various herbs to make potions and powders, and are used only once or twice in case their medicinal ingredients should be boiled away.

The comparison of brachiopods with birds has analogies in Central Europe where some Permian forms known as rhynchonellids also have outstretched 'wings' and have been likened in the past to miniature doves. One species from the Carnic

Shih-yen *(stone swallow)*; Cyrtospirifer *sp. from Devonian rocks of China (x 1 approx.)*

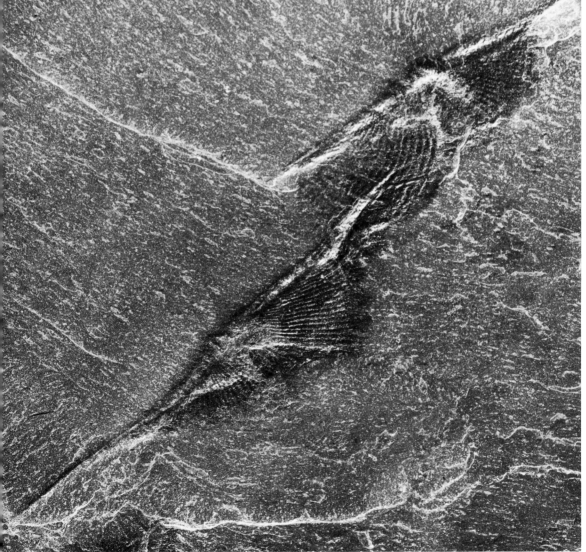

Delabole butterflies; Cyrtospirifer verneuili *from the Devonian of Old Delabole Quarry, Cornwall (x 1 approx.)*

Alps is named *Camarophoria spiritisanctus* 'in honour of the Holy Ghost'. Similar shells from the Jura Mountains are sometimes called *'Little Doves'*.

Government Rock

Not all brachiopods have the wide-hinged or winged outline of *Cyrtospirifer* and similar forms. Many groups, and in particular the terebratulids, are referred to as *lamp shells* since in side view they may resemble the type of old lamp often known as an Aladdin's lamp. In Shropshire, however, one particular genus has such distinctive features that the rock in which it occurs has been given its own unique local name. The brachiopod is *Pentamerus oblongus* which occurs so commonly in parts of Shropshire in beds of Llandovery (Silurian) age that the beds are known as the *Pentamerus* Beds. *Pentamerus* and its close relatives are characterised by the presence in the larger or pedicle valve of a spoon- or trough-shaped structure known as a spondylium, which was usually supported on the floor of the shell by a low septum or ridge. The spondylium was used as an attachment point for the muscles employed in the articulation of the brachiopod valves.

The preservation of *Pentamerus* in Shropshire is often one in which the original shell material has been dissolved away to leave impressions of the fossils in the sediments as internal and external moulds. The longitudinal spondylium and septum are preserved as a long slit in the rock connected at one end to the two slits representing the former walls of the shell. In plan view the result is to produce a single, arrow-shaped slit or mould. The presence of numerous of these outlines often closely spaced in a single rock bed was reminiscent to local people of the arrow symbol used commonly by government departments, and notably on prison uniforms. The *Pentamerus* Beds thus became known as *Government Rock*.

Chinese bean-sprouts

In parts of China and Japan, one modern brachiopod living on tidal mud flats is collected as a culinary delicacy. This is the genus *Lingula*, a spade-shaped form that lives with its beak downwards in a burrow in the mud and uses its fleshy stalk or pedicle to draw itself upwards and downwards in the burrow. The pedicle gives the brachiopod the colloquial Chinese name *Hai Dou-ya*, meaning *sea bean-sprout*. Fossil lingulids have the same general shape and are therefore referred to in some areas by the same name; the soft pedicle decays on death and is not preserved in the fossil forms, but examples are known in which the outline is preserved as an impression in the rock, thus furthering the comparison with the modern *Lingula*.

Cat Skulls

Stromatoporoids are an extinct group of fossils that are best known from rocks of Ordovician to Devonian age, although they extended through into Mesozoic strata. Details of their affinities are unclear,

Government Rock; internal moulds of the brachiopod Pentamerus oblongus *from the Pentamerus Beds, Norbury, Shropshire (x 1 approx.)*

*Hai Dou-ya (sea bean-sprouts); lingulid brachiopods from China. The two drawings (**left** and **centre**) show a fossil specimen and a modern example, respectively, both in life orientation and with the pedicle attached; the fossil specimen (**right**) is Lingula orientalis from rocks of Silurian age, shown in the orientation usually adopted for scientific descriptions − in life the pedicle emerged from the top margin*

Cat Skulls (kattskallar); *stromatoporoids from Silurian rocks of Gotland, Sweden. The outcrop* (left) *shows numerous specimens weathering out from a bed of marlstone; a single specimen* (right) *has been split to show the typical internal growth pattern – this specimen is approximately 20 centimetres long. (Photographs by courtesy of Sven Laufeld and Stig Lindbom)*

although they have been compared in the past with various colonial animal groups such as corals and sponges. The network of fine, calcareous, transverse layers and vertical walls of these fossils is built up into laminar, hemispherical or domed shapes, sometimes forming extensive masses within reefs but also occurring commonly as discrete colonies in beds of marl and limestone. In Silurian rocks on the Swedish island of Gotland such isolated, domed stromatoporoids are particularly abundant, often weathering out freely from marly beds, and in size and shape these specimens can bear a striking resemblance to bald heads or skulls; the popular Swedish name for the Gotland stromatoporoids is *kattskallar* or *cat skulls*.

In the local dialect of Gotland (Gutnian) stromatoporoids are also referred to sometimes as *kitel,* the equivalent of the Swedish word *körtel,* meaning gland. The term is applied to any nodular or globular fossil or lump of rock that resembles glands such as kidneys or hearts, particularly when such nodular masses are left after limestone has been burnt in a kiln.

Unicorns and Dragons

The mystical significance to man in the past of many of the groups of invertebrate fossils stemmed from the fact that modern representatives were unfamiliar to him in his every-day life, either because the groups were extinct or because they occupied environments such as the offshore marine areas that were inaccessible to him. In contrast, the remains of fossil vertebrate animals were much more readily recognisable as being related to living vertebrates, especially those that lived on land, so that in general there was less superstition or folklore attached to them. Of course there were exceptions, most notably in the attempts to recognise and reconstruct such mythical animals as unicorns and dragons.

Early Classical and Medieval beliefs that the pulverised horn of the fabled unicorn acted as a powerful medicine led to extensive efforts to discover specimens. Modern cow and rhinoceras horn were long passed off as substitutes, but by the Middle Ages the long, corkscrew-like horn of the narwhal became accepted as genuine. Then in about 1600 the fossil remains of some woolly mammoths from the Ice Age were found in Europe and 'experts' identified the tusks as those of the true unicorn. Almost immediately narwhal tusks were decried as *unicornum falsum,* and the mammoths became *unicornum verum.* Western man continued to believe in the validity of the unicorn until about the end of the 17th Century, and in 1663 the Mayor of Magdeburg in Germany, Otto von Guericke, made the first attempt at a reconstruction based mainly on mammoth bones from a large find in a quarry near Quedlinburg. In 1827 the French zoologist George Cuvier showed that the unicorn was a zoological impossibility, and since the true nature of the fossil mammoths had then been discovered the myth gradually disappeared into history.

In addition to the mammoth, the bones of various other Tertiary and Pleistocene mammals such as the cave-bear, the mastodon and the sabre-toothed tiger were long regarded in some regions as dragon bones, again thought to have strong medicinal properties. Such beliefs in China date back to well over 1000 B.C., and even today the names *Lung-gu (dragon bone)* and *Lung-chi (dragon teeth)* are used for some fossil mammals, the latter in particular for the teeth of the three-toed horse *Hipparion.*

Remains of the large Mesozoic reptiles have received remarkably little attention in folk history,

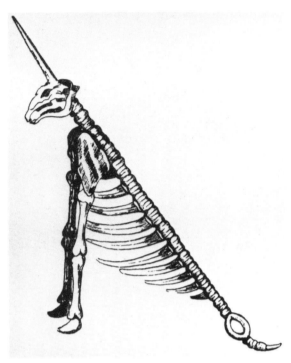

Otto von Guericke's reconstruction of a unicorn (1663) as published by Gottfried von Leibniz in his Protogaea *(1749)*

Seal of the former Street Urban District Council, Somerset (by courtesy of Mendip District Council)

but two examples from Britain with recent associations are worthy of note. The marine ichthyosaurs were once interpreted as *fossil sea-dragons,* but they have long been identified correctly as reptiles with a dolphin-like shape. In the latter part of the 19th Century numerous virtually complete ichthyosaur skeletons were quarried from the Lower Lias (Jurassic) rocks around Street in Somerset, and with time this fossil came to be used as an emblem of the town; it is still used on roadside signs welcoming visitors to Street, and was incorporated in the seal of the Urban District Council until that body ceased to exist in 1974. Quarrying operations in other parts of Britain during the 19th Century also revealed many specimens of Jurassic ichthyosaurs, and the reports of the finds of these striking fossils often caused excitement among the general public. The familiarity to the public was reflected in the publication of a cartoon and poem in *Punch* in February 1885, entitled *Ballad of the Ichthyosaurus*; here the ichthyosaur drew particular attention to one of his most distinctive morphological features, his eye, but lamented the fact that his brain was too poorly developed to allow him to achieve greater things:

> I abide in a goodly Museum
> Frequented by sages profound,
> In a kind of a strange mausoleum,
> Where the beasts that have vanished abound,
> There's a bird of the Ages Triassic
> With his antediluvian beak,
> And many a reptile Jurassic,
> And many a monster antique!
>
> Ere Man was developed, our brother,
> We swam, and we ducked, and we dived,
> And we dined, as a rule, on each other.
> What matter, the toughest survived!
> Our paddles were fins, and they bore us
> Through water, – in air we could fly;
> But the brain of the Ichthyosaurus
> Was never a match for his eye!
>
> The geologists, active and eager,
> Its excellence hasten to own,
> And praise, with no eulogy meagre,
> The eye that is plated with bone!
> 'See how, with unerring precision,
> His prey through the waves he could spy;
> Oh, wonderful organ of vision,
> Gigantic and beautiful eye!'
>
> Then I listen in gloomy dejection,
> I gaze, and I wish I could weep,

For what is mere visual perfection
To Intellect, subtle and deep?
A loftier goal is before us,
For higher endowments we sigh,
But – the brain of the Ichthyosaurus
Was never a patch on his eye!

It owned no supreme constitution,
Was shallow, and simple, and plain,
While mark the fair convolution
And size of the Aryan brain!
'Tis furnished for School-Board inspections,
And garnished for taking degrees,
And bulging in many directions,
As every phrenologist sees.

Sometimes it explodes at high pressure
In harsh, overwhelming demand,
But, plied in unmerciful measure,
It's wonderful what it will stand!
In cottage, in college, and mansion
Bear witness the girls and the boys
How great are its powers of expansion,
How very peculiar its joys!

O Brain that is bulgy with learning,
O Wisdom of women and men,
O Maids for a First that are yearning,
O Youths that are lectured by WREN!
You're acquainted with Pisces and Taurus
And all sorts of beasts in the sky,
But the brain of the Ichthyosaurus
Was never so good as his eye!

Reconstructed by DARWIN or OWEN
We dwell in sweet Bloomsbury's halls,
But we couldn't have passed Little-go in
The Schools; we'd have floundered in Smalls!
Though so cleverly people restore us
We are bound to confess, with a sigh,
That the brain of the Ichthyosaurus
Was never so good as his eye!

The second British example involves the *Iguanodon*, the large Cretaceous dinosaurian reptile discovered in Tilgate Forest, Sussex in 1822 by Gideon Mantell and first described by him in 1825. In recognition of this discovery, the nearby Borough of Maidstone included a reconstruction of the *Iguanodon* in its Coat of Arms in 1949 when the College of Arms granted a Crest and Supporters in celebration of the 400th anniversary of the first charter of the town. The present Maidstone Borough Council continues to use the same device for decorative purposes.

BALLAD OF THE ICHTHYOSAURUS.

[The Ichthyosaurus laments his incomplete development and imperfect education. He aspires to better things.]

Cartoon from Punch, or the London Charivari, *February 14th, 1885*

Coat of Arms of the former Maidstone Borough Council (by courtesy of the present Maidstone Borough Council)

Three variations of the heraldic device used as the Coat of Arms of Maidstone, all incorporating the figure of an Iguanodon *supporting the left side of the shield*

Tongue-stones

In 1616 the Italian Fabio Colonna (1567-1650) proved that objects referred to for centuries previously as *tongue-stones* or *Glossopetrae* were actually the teeth of fossil sharks. Pliny the Elder had described them as resembling a man's tongue and reported the belief that they fell from the heavens during eclipses of the moon. A different early belief was that they were the tongues of adders and that wine in which they had been soaked would form an antidote to snake-bites. This latter legend is associated particularly with the island of Malta, where shark's teeth are common in the Tertiary rocks, many of them belonging to the genus *Carcharodon*. St. Paul was shipwrecked on Malta on his way to Rome, and while there was reputedly bitten by an adder that he shook off into a fire; he is then supposed to have cast a curse on all snakes on the island, turning their forked tongues into stone to deprive them of their venom. On Malta these fossils are still known as *Ilsien San Pawl (St. Paul's tongues),* and they are often referred to in old literature as *Linguae Melitenses* or *Linguae Sancti Pauli*.

The belief in the powers of tongue-stones persists today in some parts of Italy, where they are carried to give protection against the Evil Eye. In some areas of rural Britain fossil sharks' teeth were also used for centuries to ward off cramp and rheumatism.

Toad-stones

The origin of stones known in folklore as *toad-stones* is similar to that of *glossopetrae* in that they are also the teeth of fossil fish, but in this case they are mostly the palatal teeth of rays of Mesozoic and Tertiary age. The best known examples were the small, bluish, grey or brownish stud-like teeth of the Jurassic genus *Lepidotus*, long referred to as *Bufonites* and believed to be the jewel formed in the head of a toad. This was the jewel mentioned by Duke Frederick in Shakespeare's *As you like it*:

> Sweet are the uses of adversity
> Which, like the toad, ugly and venomous,
> Wears yet a precious jewel in his head.

These *Bufonites* were often set in rings, pendants or lockets in the Middle Ages and were believed to have magical curative properties. A locket found in Devizes in Wiltshire in 1883 was made from two palatal teeth of *Lepidotus* joined by an ornamental metal band and with a tiny key hole cut in one of the teeth; it probably dates from the 16th Century.

Legend suggested that for medicinal purposes the stone had to be removed from the head of an old toad while he was still alive, although it was also believed that if the toad was placed on a red cloth then it would eject the stone itself. Various other palatal teeth such as those of *Mylioblatis* were used in medicine, probably administered as a powder, and used particularly to counteract poison and in the treatment of epilepsy.

A toad-stone; palatal teeth of the fossil ray Mylioblatis, *Barton Beds (Tertiary, Eocene), Hampshire (x 2)*

A tongue-stone (glossopetra); *views of both sides of a fossil shark's tooth,* Carcharodon megalodon *from Tertiary (Eocene) rocks, U.S.A. (x 0.75 approx.)*

Medieval woodcuts (1497) showing the supposed removal and administration of toad-stones

Crows' Nests

In contrast to the many different fossil animals with associations in folklore, or with distinctive colloquial names, very few fossil plants appear to have received the same attention. The roots or stems of fossil trees from the Coal Measures known as *Stigmaria* were popularly regarded as parts of fossil fish or serpents until fairly recently. One of the earliest illustrations of a *Stigmaria* was given by Plot who compared it with a fresh-water fish which 'seems to represent a *Carp* or *Barbel*'.

Some of the largest and best-preserved fossil trees found in Britain are in the well known Fossil Forest in the Purbeck Beds (Jurassic) at Lulworth Cove in Dorset. Here the beds of the Portland Stone are overlain directly by a bed known as the Hard Cap, which is a band of tufaceous limestone; on this is a Dirt-bed composed of black earth and pebbles representing a fossil soil deposit. In this soil, some 150 million years ago grew fairly large Cycad trees up to about 1 metre in diameter. After the trees had died, many of them remained upright during the process of fossilisation and many of the stumps took on a bowl-shaped outline due to the more rapid weathering of the centre of the trunks. The stumps were eventually enveloped by the next layers of calcareous sediments which were probably deposited by the action of freshwater algae in the shallow seas that flooded the area. At some time following their death the original material of the tree stumps was replaced by silica carried in suspension by percolating ground water, thus strengthening them and enhancing their preservation as fossils. The weathering away of the soft limestone cap has now exposed the fossil tree stumps which retain their bowl-shape, and which are known locally from this shape as fossil *Birds' Nests* or *Crows' Nests*.

Acknowledgements

A number of people have kindly given me information and comments that have improved or amplified this article; they are too numerous to mention individually but I thank them all for their kindness. In particular, however, I am grateful to Dr. Mee-Mann Chang for providing me with details and illustrations relating to fossil folklore in China, and to Mr. Aubrey Cherns for his help in tracing the use of ammonites in architecture.

Further reading

The following list is not a comprehensive bibliography but is intended to draw attention to some of the more interesting publications that will allow the reader to study further details of some of the topics covered in this article. The books by Rudwick, Adams, Edwards and Wendt include chapters on the different interpretations of fossils through historical times, while the other papers cover more specific subjects.

ADAMS, F.D. 1955. *The birth and development of the geological sciences.* 506 pages, Dover Publications, New York. [First edition 1938]

EDWARDS, W.N. 1967. *The early history of palaeontology.* 58 pages, Trustees of the British Museum (Natural History), London.

HOWE, S.R., SHARPE, T. and TORRENS, H.S. 1981. *Ichthyosaurs: a history of fossil 'sea-dragons'.* 32 pages, National Museum of Wales, Cardiff.

KENNEDY, C.B. 1976. A fossil for what ails you: the remarkable history of fossil medicine. *Fossils Magazine,* volume 1, issue 1, pages 42-57.

NELSON, C.M. 1968. Ammonites: Ammon's Horns into Cephalopods. *Journal of the Society for the Bibliography of Natural History,* volume 5, pages 1-18.

OAKLEY, K.[P.] 1965. Folklore of fossils. *Antiquity,* volume 39, pages 9-16, plates 1,2 (part 1), pages 117-125, plates 21-26 (part 2).

OAKLEY, K.P. 1975. Decorative and symbolic uses of vertebrate fossils. *Pitt Rivers Museum, University of Oxford, Occasional Papers on Technology, 12,* pages 1-60, plates 1-10.

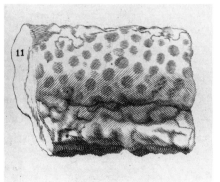 

Robert Plot's 'Carp or Barbel' (left) *from* The Natural History of Oxfordshire, *with a similar portion* (right) *of* Stigmaria ficoides *from the Upper Carboniferous Coal Measures of South Wales for comparison (x 0.5 approx.)*

Crows' Nests; the fossilised stumps of trees in the fossil forest, Lulworth Cove, Dorset (from The Dorset Coast, A Geological Guide, G. M. Davies, 1964)

REGNÉLL, G. 1949. On the position of palaeontology and historical geology in Sweden before 1800. *Arkiv för Mineralogi och Geologi,* volume 1, pages 1-64.

RUDWICK, M.J.S. 1973. *The meaning of fossils: episodes in the history of palaeontology.* xii + 287 pages, History of Science Library, Macdonald, London and American Elsevier Inc., New York.

SKEAT, W.W. 1912. 'Snakestones' and stone thunderbolts as subjects for systematic investigation. *Folk-lore,* volume 23, pages 45-80.

SWINTON, W.E. 1960. Early history of comparative anatomy. *Endeavour,* volume 19, pages 209-214.

TAYLOR, M.E. and ROBISON, R.A. 1976. Trilobites in Utah folklore. *Brigham Young University Geology Studies,* volume 23, pages 1-5.

WENDT, H. 1970. *Before the deluge.* 428 pages, Paladin, London.

GEOLOGICAL TIME SCALE

ERA		PERIOD	AGE (Millions of years ago)	Summary of geological history of Wales
CENOZOIC	QUATERNARY	Recent or Holocene	0.01 – present	Coastal areas drowned by rising sea level caused by melting ice at the end of the Ice Age. Deposits of alluvium and peat, with further development of present drainage patterns and modern flora and fauna.
		Pleistocene	1.6 – 0.01	The 'Ice Age', with repeated glaciations and milder interglacial periods. The most recent major glaciation reached a maximum 18,000 years ago, and the last local ice left North Wales by 14,500 years ago. Modification of land forms by ice scouring and deposition of glacial drift. First evidence of Man in Wales from Pontnewydd cave, North Wales, about 200,000 years old.
	TERTIARY	Neogene	26 – 1.6	Prolonged, pulsatory uplift and erosion. Late Palaeogene and early Neogene terrestrial sediments known only from Mochras and locally in Gwynedd and south-west Dyfed. Early Palaeogene intrusive igneous rocks in north-west Wales. Basic landforms and drainage patterns established.
		Palaeogene	65 – 26	
MESOZOIC		Cretaceous	140 – 65	No rocks of this age known in Wales. Different opinions suggest either a persistence of terrestrial conditions, or that the Chalk sea covered much of the country.
		Jurassic	195 – 140	Lower Jurassic marine rocks known only from south-east Glamorgan and Mochras borehole, Harlech, with thick, younger sediments in Bristol Channel. Warm, shallow sea may have transgressed over Wales through the period but direct evidence is lacking.
		Triassic	230 – 195	Arid and semi-arid terrestrial conditions, with evidence of periodic flash floods. Dinosaur footprints and early mammal remains known from Glamorgan. Marine transgression in south-east Wales at the very end of the period.
PALAEOZOIC	UPPER	Permian	280 – 230	Uplift and mountain building (Hercynian Orogeny). Erosion across most of Wales.
		Carboniferous	345 – 280	Marine transgression early in period, leading to spread of warm, subtropical seas with rich coral/brachiopod faunas; extensive deposition of carbonate sediments that now form the Carboniferous Limestone. Regression in middle of period, with widespread deltaic deposits. Rich vegetation on coastal plains and deltas in late Carboniferous times; peat accumulated to form coal seams of the Coal Measures.
		Devonian	395 – 345	Uplift and mountain building (Caledonian Orogeny) continued from Silurian times, resulting in the deposition of the terrestrial Old Red Sandstone across most of Wales. Rapid diversification of land floras and non-marine fish faunas.
	LOWER	Silurian	435 – 395	Marine muds, silts and sands, with local carbonate sediments. Land with deltas across South Wales. Shallowing and retreat of the sea late in the period, with widespread onset of terrestrial conditions. Earliest fishes in Wales, and first vascular land plants appeared.
		Ordovician	505 – 435	Marine muds, sands, grits and local carbonate sediments. Evidence of extensive volcanicity in north, mid and south-west Wales. Fossil faunas increasingly diverse, including first corals.
		Cambrian	570 – 505	Transgression of sea into Wales, with deposition of grits, sands and muds. First abundant fossils, including earliest trilobites and brachiopods.
PRECAMBRIAN			4600 – 570	Oldest rocks in Wales dated at about 600-700 million years old, but are possibly considerably older. Evidence of intermittent marine conditions and volcanicity, with periods of folding, uplift and erosion. Earliest fossils from Wales are 'jellyfish' from Carmarthen of late Precambrian age.